JOYCE visits GRANNY

Tswiri Book No. 2
Published by Biograph Co. Pty. Ltd.
Craighall, Johannesburg.
Written by Joan Solomon 1975©
Photographs by R. Harvey.
ISBN 0 620 01420 2.

Acknowledgements:
This series of publications is made possible by grants
from Misereor, Anglo American Corporation and
De Beers Consolidated Mines. Assistance has
unstintingly been given by the S.A. Bureau of
Literacy and Literature.

Printed by:
Supreme Printers Johannesburg.

Distributed by:
The S.A. Bureau of Literacy and
Literature, 403 Dunwell,
35 Jorissen St., Braamfontein, 2001, Johannesburg.

JOYCE visits GRANNY

A TSWIRI BOOK

Joyce and her aunt,
whose name is Nomsa,
have come to visit Granny
in the village.

Sipho runs to meet Aunt Nomsa. She is Sipho's mother. Sipho and his brother Lolo live with Granny. There is Lolo on Granny's back.

Granny and Mokgadi welcome Nomsa.
They are filled with joy
to see her and Joyce.

"Ah, there is little Joyce"
says Grandpa.
"What a big girl
you are now."

Aunt Nomsa has brought presents
for the family.
"Joyce, take the presents
out of the packet for Granny,"
says Aunt Nomsa.
Sipho gets in the way.

There is much to be
done in the house.
Aunt Nomsa likes
to help Granny.
"Sipho, you and
Joyce go and play."

They swing on the farm gate.
"Look Joyce,
there's the baby lamb," says Sipho.

Sipho holds the lamb's legs
because he wants Malufi
to put him down.
"Touch him gently,"
says Malufi.
"He is only two days old."

They go to
Uncle Pholo's yard.

"Let us play here, Joyce.
When Uncle comes
he may give us a ride."

Uncle Pholo takes Joyce and Sipho
for a ride in his donkey-cart.
Sipho cries when the ride is over.
"Never mind,"
says Joyce.
"Never mind, Sipho."

"Come Sipho, I will show you
I am not afraid of cows."

"Do not go too close,"
says Joyce.

"They wont hurt us,"
says Sipho.
"Look, the baby
is drinking from
its mother."

Joyce and Sipho
have their lunch.

Then they play on the cart
in the yard.
Sipho is the driver.

The big girls are back from school.
They play a game
which some girls call *"diketo"*
and others call *"izigamtho"*.

Granny takes Joyce and Sipho
for a walk.
"Do you know what the
church bell says, Joyce?"
"It says,
Tong-Tong
Tong-Tong."

When it is cool
they go to the
water-pump. Kifelwe
makes the pump work, while Granny
collects the water in her bucket.

It is late
when they return.
The sheep are already
in their pen.

The day is over.
Joyce and Aunt Nomsa
must leave.

"Good-bye Granny.
Good-bye Sipho."
Everyone waves.

The bus takes Joyce and Aunt Nomsa home.

"What did you do at Granny's house?" asks Mother. Father and Thabu also want to know. "I played with Sipho," says Joyce, "and I saw the lamb and I saw the cows walking on the grass. Granny says Thabu must come with me next time."